W9-AKY-336

Hidden in the Desert of the Dying Tree
lies a town run by ruthless killers,
a growing cancer upon the vast
and volatile fantasy world of Asunda.

Some say it's a watering hole for the Devil.

A Stranger has returned to Oasis.
A deal has been made.

THE UNTAMED

A Sinner's Prayer

WRITER
  SEBASTIAN A. JONES
ARTIST
  PETER BERGTING
LAYOUT ARTIST
  DARRELL MAY
LETTERERS AND DESIGNERS
  A LARGER WORLD STUDIOS
  & CHRISTOPHER GARNER
ASUNDA FONT
  CHRISTOPHER WALMSLEY
EDITOR
  JOSHUA COZINE

ASSOCIATES
  KEN LOCSMANDI
  MARK HAMMOND
  TERRANCE BOULDIN-JOHNSON
CHIEF CREATIVE OFFICER
  DARRELL MAY
EDITOR-IN-CHIEF
  JOSHUA COZINE
PUBLISHER
  SEBASTIAN A. JONES

BASED IN THE WORLD OF ASUNDA CREATED BY SEBASTIAN A. JONES

COPYRIGHT © 2017 SEBASTIAN A. JONES AND STRANGER COMICS LLC. ALL RIGHTS RESERVED. THE WORLD OF ASUNDA, CHARACTERS, MYTHOS, AND THE ENVIRONMENT IN THE UNTAMED: A SINNER'S PRAYER, AND THE DISTINCTIVE LIKENESSES THEREOF ARE PROPERTIES OF SEBASTIAN A. JONES AND STRANGER COMICS LLC, [STRANGER COMICS OWNS AN EXCLUSIVE LICENSE FROM SEBASTIAN A. JONES] AND ARE THE PRODUCT OF THE AUTHOR'S IMAGINATION. NO SIMILARITY BETWEEN ANY OF THE NAMES, CHARACTERS, PERSONS AND/OR INSTITUTIONS WITH THOSE OF ANY LIVING OR DEAD PERSON OR INSTITUTION IS INTENDED, AND ANY SUCH SIMILARITY WHICH MAY EXIST IS PURELY COINCIDENTAL. NO PORTION OF THIS PUBLICATION MAY BE REPRODUCED OR TRANSMITTED, IN ANY FORM OR BY ANY MEANS, WITHOUT THE EXPRESS WRITTEN PERMISSION OF SEBASTIAN A. JONES AND STRANGER COMICS LLC. PATHFINDER CONTENT SUBJECT TO WIZARDS OF THE COAST OPEN GAME LICENSE © 2010 AS DETAILED AT PAIZO.COM/PATHFINDERRPG/PRD/OPENGAMELICENSE.HTML

FIRST PRINTING. PRINTED IN SOUTH KOREA. ISBN 978-1-939834-31-7

UWALEK

GAO

Massa

OR

Ugoa

UJDA

QUESH

GULF

ERREKATH

JORIARU

ASUNDA

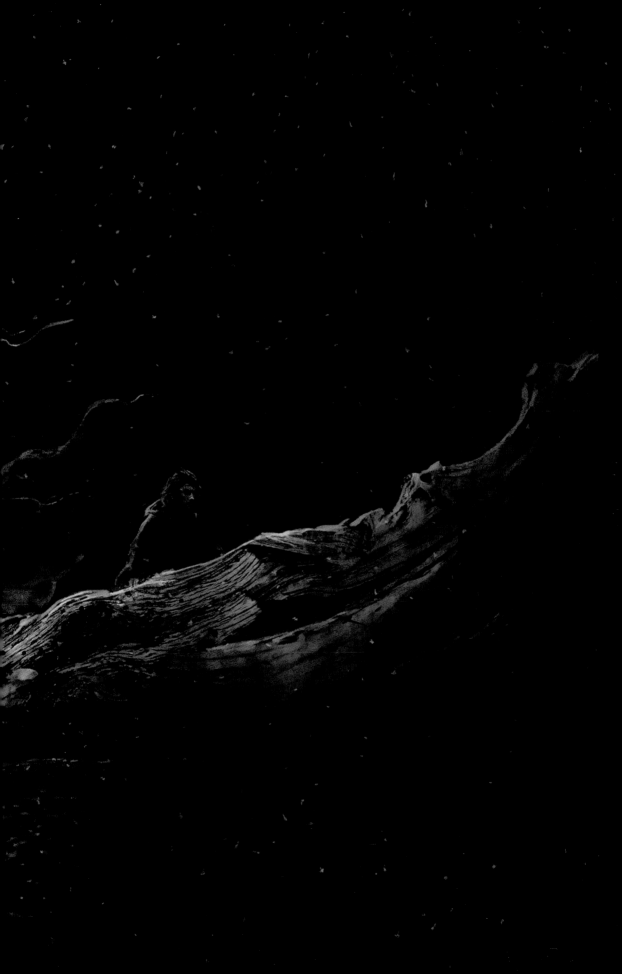

He was trapped in a world absent of color. Ghostly. He had been searching for her face in the relentless void, hell's familiar blanket that held him tight. Ten years. Give or take. But he was here now. With her. And although her wrath would be akin to the lash of a thousand teeth, he would welcome the pain… just to hear her speak his name.

In the empty, mist-filled room, she looked out an open window and up to the red turbulent sky beyond. She was a saint by those who knew her company, yet her large haunting eyes had seen much sin in her twenty-some years, for she was married to a man of ill repute, known to be a killer of men. Upon his final day, he was the demon butcher of babes and women alike, until the thud of an axe ended his terror. But she loved him. That was her curse. Some said she had been on the verge of turning him from wickedness. The second child she carried had tipped the scales, but before it could draw first breath, her world burned.

"I stand by this window every moment given. A fool waiting for a promise to descend from the storm with bowed back and bloodied knee, with love and hate as my cruel companion in truth," she said, then admitted in quiet pain as if remembering a moment spoken. "Crueler in lies."

"I have not forgotten your face as much as I have tried," offered his broken voice from beyond her reach. "Your smile. Our whisper…"

"And what of the others who hold you?" she countered.

"I am here now."

"A whisper of now is not enough."

The young woman turned slowly, a gleaming blue-black sword by her side. Her wild, coarse hair roamed beyond small shoulders to mingle with a sheer, flowing gown in a way that made his spirit stir and yearn for a life never lived. But even after a decade of dreams, there was a finality to her. Death and sex but a moment away.

She saw him then as he was, naked and kneeling before her. It was as it had been before, when he needed her comfort and forgiveness. When he was lost. Scars and burns upon his back told the decade's worth of hellish torture he had endured to find her, to see her face. But she had given much in the time before and he had failed her. She knew what he would ask, but she would not return, would no longer speak his name. Until he changed his ways, he would be a Stranger.

"Am I dead to you?" the Stranger asked.

"It matters not. Are you with me beyond?" The corner of her full lips pinched. "When the red hand snatches the final hour and all is black and ash, will you sing my name for all to hear?"

"With want," he insisted.

"Or will our song remain with forked tongue until throats bleed from raking screams? Until we are silenced by angels?"

"Feathers flayed should they try," he promised.

"My skin is a stretched canvas upon which your crimson hymns are written. A whore's lullaby. Another's song to ruin."

He dared to steal a glance from her liquid eyes as she gripped the sword's black bone hilt, her knuckles whitening.

"Jenna…"

"Yes, husband?"

"How many must I kill before the quiet?"

She sighed. "My poor love. You still do not understand. But one soul do I crave and 'tis no man living, nor lover of yours."

"Am I dead to you?"

She dropped her gown past swollen breasts and skin streaked in gold. The silk robe floated past her arm and was severed upon the rune lit blade. Pristine.

"Are you?"

Stranger's Theme
(Written by Jens Engelbrecht & Sebastian A. Jones)

SEBASTIAN A. JONES   PETER BERGTING

I'M GOING HOME.

"IT'S AN UGLY WORLD OUT THERE. WHERE ARE YOU HEADING, STRANGER?"

"THE TOWN OF OASIS."

A FREQUENT STOP.

IS IT FAR?

AS FAR AS EVERYWHERE ELSE.

I CAN FEEL THE
BITE OF EACH AND
EVERY GRAIN OF
SAND FIGHTING
BENEATH MY FEET.

BUT THEIR TOUCH IS AS
UNFAMILIAR AS A PROMISE
GIVEN TO A WOMAN I
COULD NOT FORGET.

AS MUCH AS I
HAVE TRIED.

TRIBE OF THE
DYING TREE.

CURSED WATCHMEN
BETWEEN TWO WORLDS.

HERE, THEIR SACRED TREE IS
LORD AND MASTER, DEFIANT
AGAINST THE SUN DRAKE.

IT'S A SPECIAL MOMENT WHEN YOU BLEED A MAN.

A BOND IS FORMED. JUST YOU AND HIM.
TO BREAK HIS BODY, TO GUT HIS JOY.
BUT WHAT OF HIS SPIRIT?
JENNA
ASHANI
WHEN YOU LOOK INTO HIS EYES, YOU'LL KNOW.

DUNES RISE AND FALL LIKE SLEEPING SILK, AS DAY TURNS TO NIGHT AND NIGHT TURNS TO DAY.

THE SKY WRESTLES IN TURMOIL AS I DRAW CLOSER TO THE WELL OF LIFE.

THEY DON'T WANT ME HERE.

THE TOWN OF OASIS.

MY TOWN.

THE GATE OF OASIS IS SAID TO PASS JUDGEMENT UPON ALL WHO ENTER HER HAVEN.

WE'RE ALL SINNERS.

NIGHT FALLS WITH A CHILL.

MY UNWELCOME IS NO SURPRISE.

IF YOU'RE ALONE AT THIS TIME, YOU'RE EITHER PLUM FOOLISH...

...OR ONE TO BE WARY OF.

ONLY SOME CAN TELL THE DIFFERENCE.

EDGE OF T-TOWN.

THE LACKEYS ARE NOTHING. LESSER MEN HIDING BEHIND GRIT AND COURAGE.

BRITTLE AS LEAVES BAKED IN THE SUN.

IT'S THE GRACHUKK AND THE BOY. THEIR FACES SPEAK OF MY PAST. I NEED ANSWERS.

MY SWORD SHALL ASK THE QUESTIONS.

THE GIRL LOOKS OUT OF PLACE. A GLOWING LIGHT AMIDST THE GLOOM.

SHE'D BE TOO YOUNG TO REMEMBER.

PING

"HE HAD TO BE."

PING

PING

PING

A DEAL'S A DEAL.

"SEVEN DAYS."

"SEVEN SOULS.

"SEVEN DAYS FOR SEVEN SOULS. UPON THE EIGHTH YOU SHALL HAVE EARNED YOUR FREEDOM."

"WHAT WILL HAPPEN IF I FAIL?"

"HE WILL FIND YOU."

ALE.

FOOD?

NONE LEFT.

ROOM?

OR NO LONGER
WANT TO.

Day Two

ARE PEOPLE BORN INTO THIS WORLD WITH WICKED INTENTIONS OR DO WE MOLD THEM FROM OUR OWN FEARS?

IT IS THE WOMEN WHO SPEAK OF LOVE. THAT ALL BABES ARE BORN WITH AN HONEST SOUL.

WHO TOLD THEM THESE LIES?

WHERE ARE THE WOMEN NOW? MOST HERE ARE WHORES OR WIDOWS, OR BOTH. THEY HIDE FROM THE MEN. DO THEY HIDE FROM DECEIT OR DO THEY HIDE FROM THE TRUTH?

IF YOU CARE TO LOOK YOU WILL FIND THE TRUTH, AND YOU WILL BE REPULSED.

THE KRAVEN.

ARE YOU WITH THEM?

I WAS. A LONG TIME AGO.

THEY TOOK SOMETHING FROM ME ALSO. I AM HERE TO COLLECT.

THEN I WILL TELL YOU WHAT I KNOW...

"...THORNE."

MEMORY IS COMING BACK IN BROKEN SHARDS, TEARING AT THE EDGES OF MY MIND.

RIP OUT HIS SPLEEN AND FEED IT TO THE DOGS. BETTER YET, TAKE THE WRETCH TO THE PRIEST.

HOW WE LIVE IS AS FLEETING AS INNOCENCE. HOW WE DIE IS ALL THAT REALLY MATTERS.

HE SHALL BURN!

"BEING DEAD WILL BE THE LEAST OF THE DEAD'S WORRIES..."

"TONIGHT WE ARE AS ONE. FOR TONIGHT WE FEAST ON THE FLESH OF THE LIVING AND REVEL IN THE SOULS OF THE DEAD!"

"WRITHE IN THE PERVERSE NIRVANA THAT IS THIS NIGHT, FOR TOMORROW IS NOT YET PROMISED..."

YOU ALL KNOW HIM. HE RULES WITH MIGHT. HIS KILL IS OUR DELIGHT.

FOR HE IS OUR DELIVERER, OFFERING THE BLISS OF IGNORANT FORNICATION FOR THOSE WHOSE SWORDS NEED SHEATHING.

"GOLDEN FRUITS RIPE FOR THE PLUCKING FOR A JOB WELL DONE.

"BUT BE WARY, GENTLEMEN AND GENTLER WOMEN, HE COULD JUST AS EASILY TENDER A CLOUD-FILLED ROAD TO OBLIVION FOR ALL WHO DARE TAMPER WITH HIS SANCTUARY!"

LARIEL. SHE HA-HAS THAT EFFECT ON PEOPLE.

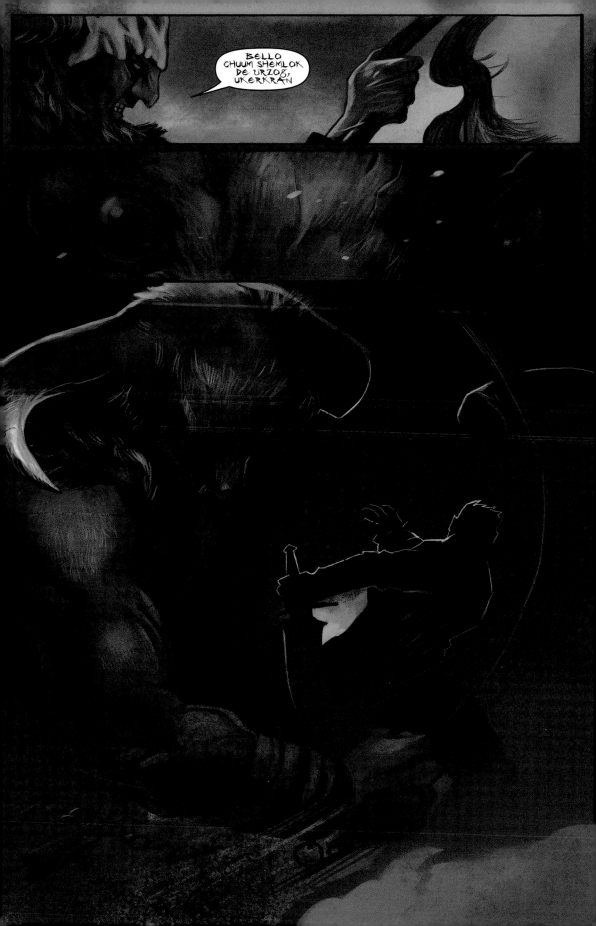

I NEVER FEEL SORRY FOR KILLING BAD MEN. WE'LL MEET AGAIN SOON. THEY'LL HAVE THEIR CHANCE.
IT'S THE NAME HE SPOKE. LARIEL. EVEN WHEN I HURT HIM THE MOST HE WOULDN'T TALK ABOUT HER.
THIS PRIEST MUST HAVE MORE POWER THAN ANY ONE MAN SHOULD POSSESS.
COME NOW. LET'S STOP THIS PLAY...
I WAS JUST DOING WHAT I WAS TOLD. IT WAS PHYLAX, HE WAS THE ONE. IT WASN'T ME. I WAS YOUR FRIEND...

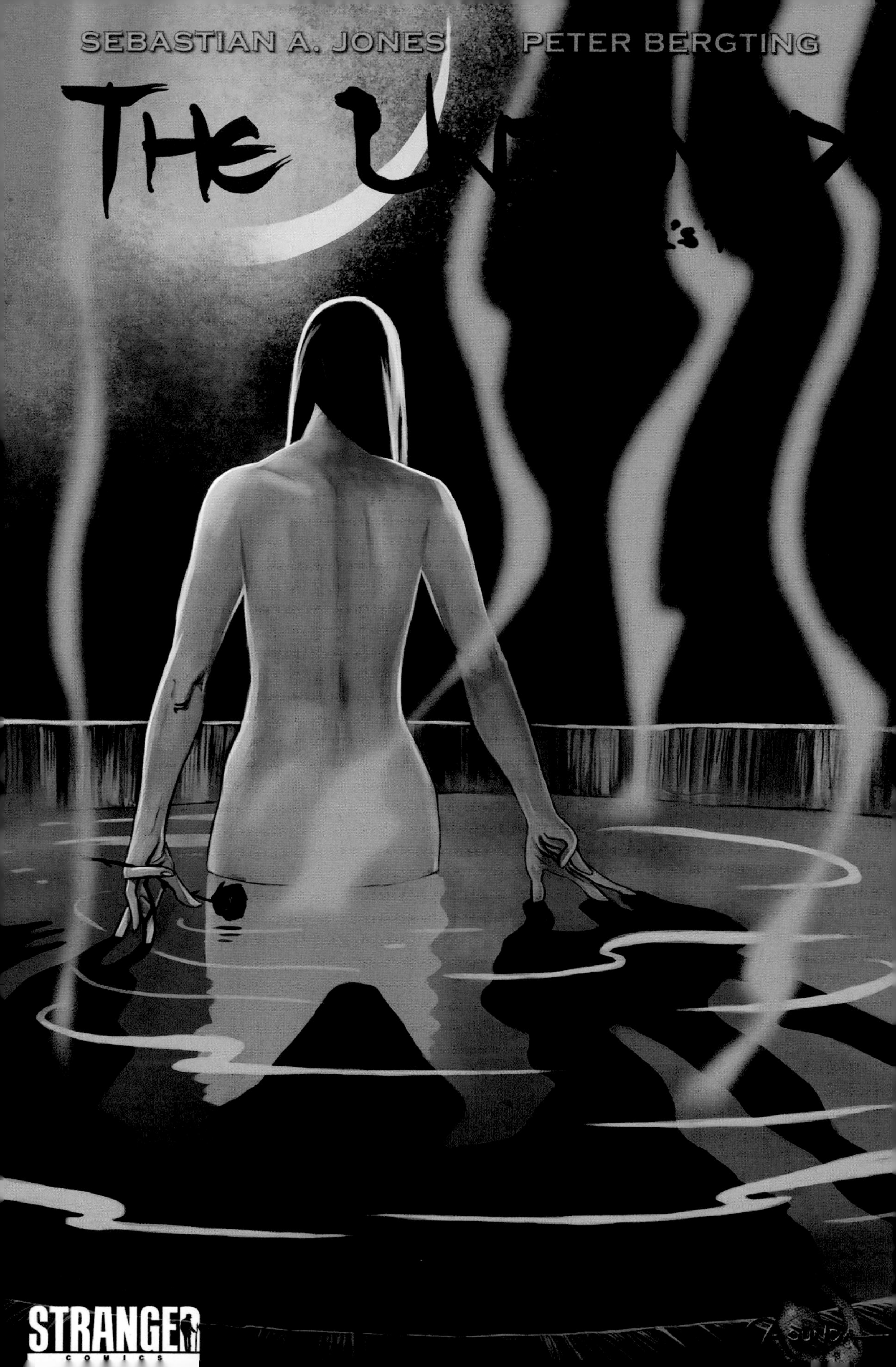
SEBASTIAN A. JONES
PETER BERGTING
THE
STRANGER
COMICS

I LEAVE YOU AS YOU LEFT ME... DISJOINTED, AFRAID, AND ALONE AMONG THE REFUSE.
YOU HAVE A CHOICE TO MAKE.
I PLAY A FAMILIAR TUNE. ONE NOT HEARD SINCE HE WAS A BOY.
I LISTEN TO HIM WAIL.

PHYLAX. I'LL BREAK OUT THE GOOD STUFF.

HELLO, MOLLY. FANCY A ROLL LATER?

YOU'LL GET YOUR SEVEN MINUTES.

HOW'S THE ARM?

LARIEL. SHE FI-FIXED IT GOOD.

SHOULD HAVE GONE TO MOLLY. SHE'D HAVE THROWN IN A TREAT. MADE IT FEEL ALL BETTER.

YOU MADE OUT WELL THE OTHER NIGHT.

W-WE ALL DID, THANKS TO YOU.

BETTER THAN THORNE.

THE BOYS ARE STILL LOOKING FOR HIS EARS.

MAYBE KER-KERSHEG HAS THEM ON HIS NECKLACE. YOU SHOULD ASK HIM.

YOU'RE A SMART BOY, STUTTERS. YOU ALWAYS WERE.

THERE IS NOTHING LEFT OF ME HERE.
ARNUMINEL WASHES AWAY THE PAIN OF REGRET THAT HAS LINGERED TOO LONG.
HER TEARS FALL FAR FROM A HEAVEN I SHALL NEVER KNOW.
THIS IS NO PLACE FOR HER AND YET STILL SHE CRIES...
SHE CRIES FOR A SINNER'S PRAYER.

TAP TAP
IF SHE LIKES IT FROM THE BACK?
WHY BO-BOTHER WITH THE FRONT. EVENING, LAUGHING JACK.
THERE'S A NEW PASSWORD, MASTER STUTTERS. WHERE HAVE YOU BEEN?
WITH BRANDY.
I LOVE HER.
WE ALL LOVE A GOOD WHORE, LAUGHING JACK.
I'LL TELL-TELL YOU A POEM. ONE SHE'D LIKE.

WON'T YOU SIT, FATHER. PLEASE.
LARIEL. YOUR NAME IS A LONGING. A HAUNTING PROMISE OF A SUMMER THAT WILL NEVER COME. YOU KEEP MEN TRAPPED IN WINTER, LARIEL.
THAT IS WHY YOU ARE RICH.
GOLD IS NOTHING COMPARED TO A LONGING.
PLEASE SIT.
BE WARY WITH YOUR WORDS, PRIEST. YOU ARE IN OUR HOME.
THE NIGHTS HAVE BEEN ENDLESS. FORGIVE.

GRATHLOK. YOU HAVE COME TO EASE MY SUFFERING MIND. OR PERHAPS TO GIVE BACK THE COIN FOR A TASK UNDONE?
I HAVE BEEN SEARCHING, AND I HAVE NOT FOUND THE ONE WE SEEK.
DO YOU STILL FEAR HIS NAME?
YES.
SPEAK IT.
YOU FORBADE HIS NAME FROM BEING UTTERED TEN YEARS AGO.
BASED ON YOUR WISDOM.
TO SPEAK THE NAME IS TO CONJURE THE DEMON.
AND YET HERE HE IS.

PERHAPS THERE IS ONE AMONG US, WHO WANTED HIM BACK...
WHO HERE STILL HOLDS THEIR HEART CLOSE TO HIS NAME?
SPEAK NOW SO WE MAY KNOW!
THIS IS NOT YOUR PULPIT AND WE ARE NOT YOUR DISCIPLES TO BUGGER WITH CHAFING POETICS.
NO. YOU ARE CERTAINLY YOUR OWN WOMAN, MY DEAR.
SPEAK UPON MY LOVE WITH DISDAIN ONCE MORE, AND I SHALL SEAR YOUR TWISTED TONGUE BEFORE YOU CAN UTTER A WORD!
I AM YOUR SERVANT.
I LICK THE SCUM OFF YOUR BOOTS WITH GLADNESS.

YOUR BROTHER IS HIDDEN FROM MY SPIRIT SIGHT. MY VISION IS BLOCKED BY A LIGHT I CANNOT PIERCE.

WHAT IS YOUR USE THEN?

HE HAS RETURNED, STRONGER THAN YOU CAN IMAGINE. HE WAS A KILLER BEFORE, ALTHOUGH HE HAD HIS WEAKNESS.

NOW WITH THE BLESSING OF THE DAMNED, HE IS ALMOST...

WHAT WAS HIS WEAKNESS?

LOVE.

SEND FOR SKARLOK TWO HEARTS.

THE MORKAI ASSASSIN IS MORE DANGEROUS THAN EVEN YOUR BROTHER, AND LOVES ME LESS THAN YOU.

THEN SEND FOR OTHER SILVER ELVES. SEE TO IT THEY FIND HIM OR BE PREPARED TO MEET THE ONE YOU SERVE.

IF THE MORKAI FAIL, WE WILL ALL MAKE THE JOURNEY TO *THE UNTAMED* REALM OF NO TOMORROW.

BUT HAVE NO FEAR, KING OF KRAVEN...

"THEY WILL KILL A DEAD MAN."
WE WILL HAVE ONE MORE FOR DINNER.
A FRIEND, I HOPE?
YOUR BROTHER DES-DESPISES YOU.
WHAT DID YOU TELL HIM?
THAT I WOULD BE-BETRAY YOU.
KERSHEG HAS YOUR SCENT.
WERE YOU FOLLOWED?
NO.
STUTTERS, THIS IS NIOBE.
WOULD YOU BETRAY US?

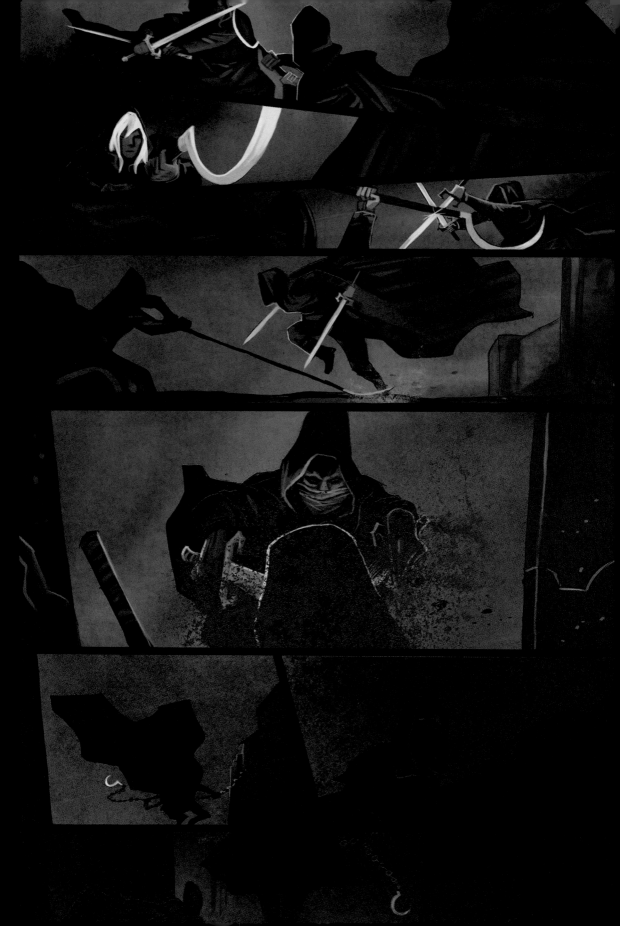

IT WOULD SEEM *THE UNTAMED* DOES NOT WANT THE MOTHER MOON TO INTERFERE, MORKAI.

I DO NOT NEED *MAGGA'S* BLESSING TO KILL YOU, MORTAL.

I HAVE CHANGED.

MY LIFE IS A SHADOW THAT DEEPENS IN DEATH.

SEBASTIAN A. JONES   PETER BERGTING

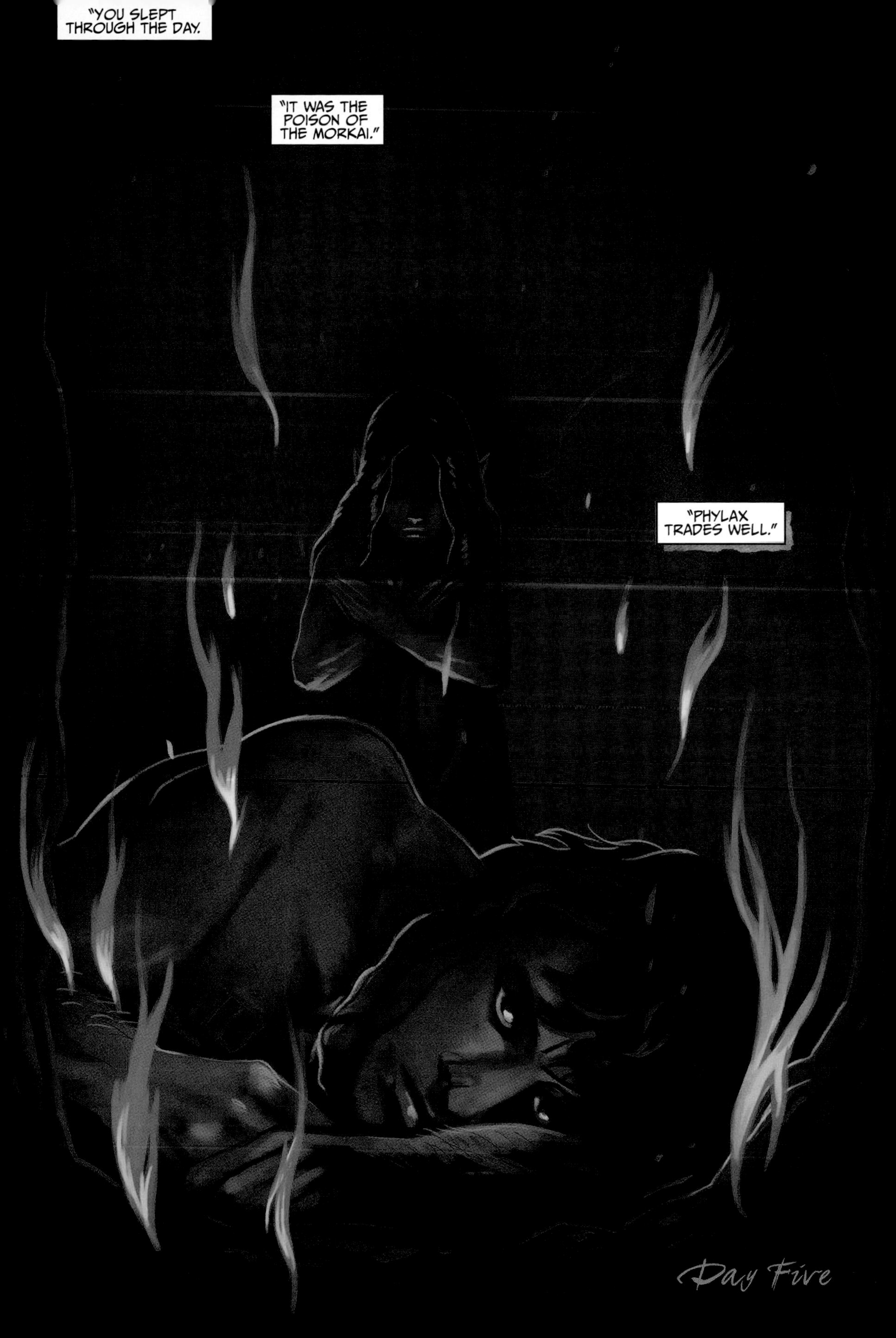
"YOU SLEPT THROUGH THE DAY.
"IT WAS THE POISON OF THE MORKAI."
"PHYLAX TRADES WELL."
Day Five

TELL ME WHAT YOU KNOW OF LARIEL.
SHE BETRAYED YOU TOO?
SHE IS PHYLAX'S WOMAN. SOME SAY SHE RULES THE KING.
WHAT DO YOU SAY?
I BELIEVE THAT TRUE POWER LIES IN FAITH.
SHEEP OF FAITH FOLLOW BLINDLY. IT IS THE SHEPHERD WHO HOLDS POWER.
I AM NOT AFRAID OF YOU...
...OR YOUR SHEPHERD.

TEN YEARS AGO, I SENT MY WIFE AND CHILD FAR AWAY SO I COULD LEAD A SINNER'S LIFE...
WHEN I WAS FINISHED WITH MY EVIL WAYS...
...WHEN I WAS READY TO BE A MAN, IT WAS TOO LATE.
I LOST THE ONLY PEOPLE WHO EVER TRULY LOVED ME...
... AND RETURNED TO THOSE WHO WOULD SELL MY SOUL.

YOU ARE A DEMON.
I WAS GIVEN A SECOND CHANCE IN DEATH. VENGEANCE WAS OFFERED AND I WAS QUICK TO ACCEPT.
HAVE YOU CALLED UPON *HIM?*
IF I DO, I MAY LOSE THEM FOREVER.
THEN STAY HERE WITH ME AND LEAVE *THE DEVIL* BEYOND THE GATE.
I HAVE MADE A DEAL THAT CANNOT BE UNDONE.
WHAT IF YOU DIE AGAIN?

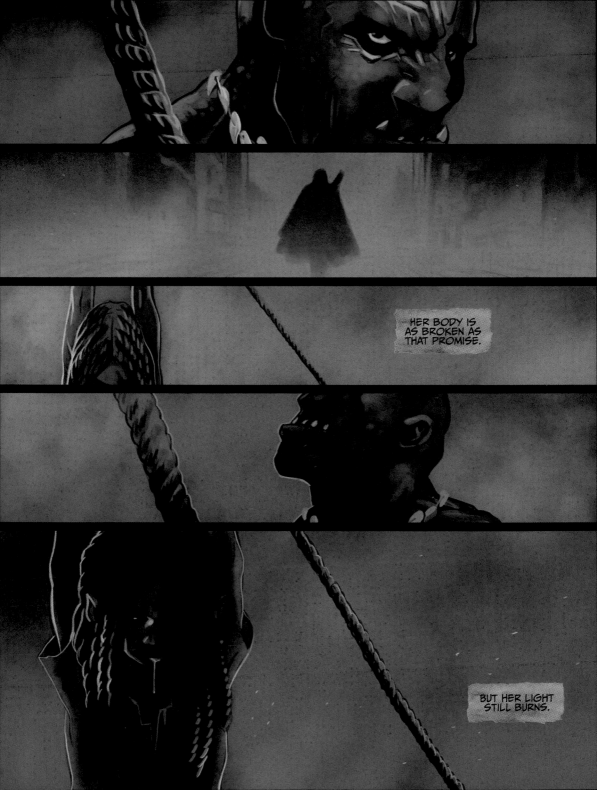

HER BODY IS
AS BROKEN AS
THAT PROMISE.

BUT HER LIGHT
STILL BURNS.

ARUKAS!
HEED MY CALL!
FREE ME OF THESE BONDS SO I CAN DELIVER MY PROMISE TO YOU.
I WILL DAMN MYSELF AND ALL OTHERS TO BATHE THIS TOWN IN BLOOD...

Stepping into the scorching sun,

She must..

With yesterday shake and tomorrow a hope

She waits..

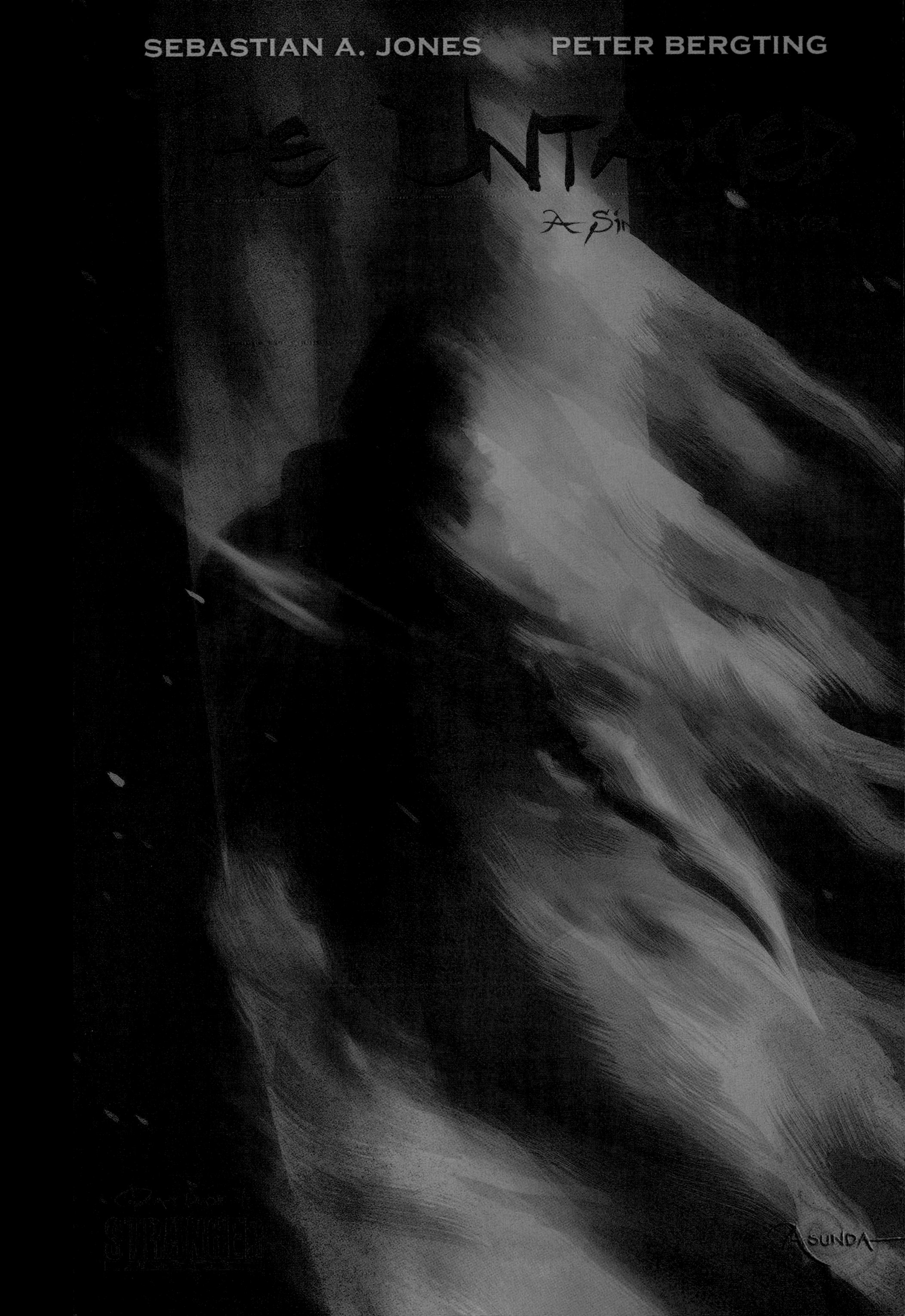
SEBASTIAN A. JONES
PETER BERGTING

I AM HERE TO SEE THE DEMON.
NO ONE IS ALLOWED UNTIL THE PRIEST COMES TO BANISH IT. ORDERS OF PHYLAX.
THEN I SHALL GO BACK TO HIS BED AND TELL HIM A TALE OF HOW LAUGHING JACK MADE ME CRY.
WHAT WOULD HIS ORDERS BE THEN?
HE WOULD KILL ME.
SLOWLY...
HRMM...

EVERYTHING...
I WILL SCREAM FOR YOU...
...LIKE THE OLD DAYS.
YOU WILL HAVE YOUR SECOND CHANCE.
GIVE ME *MINE!*

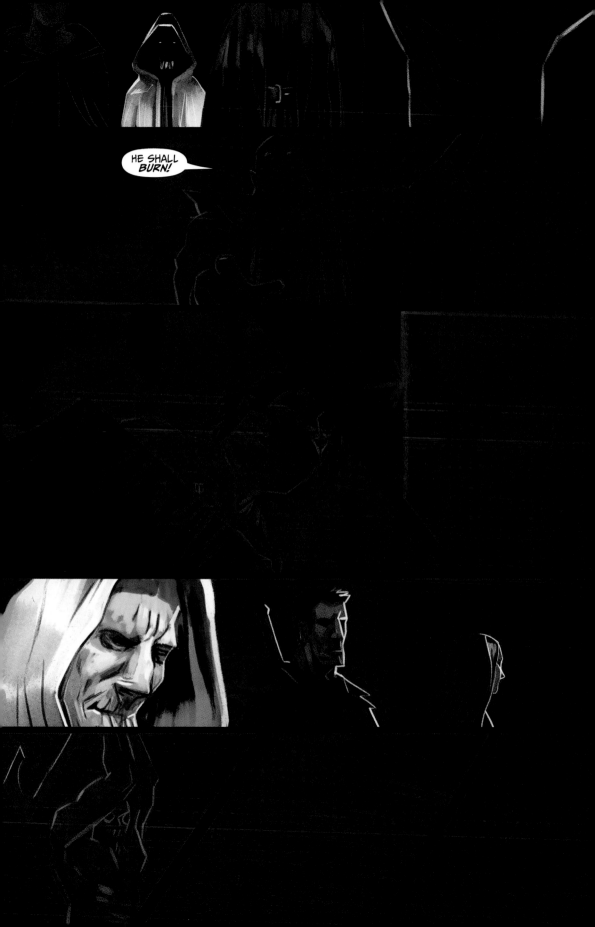

SO THE SILVER ELVES TRADED YOU MORE THAN POISON.
THE FALSE OF FAITH CALLING ON *MAGGA'S* SHADOWS...
...YOU RISK THE MOON DRAGON'S IRE.
I WOULD RISK *EVERYTHING!*

YOU DON'T HAVE THE STRENGTH.
FREE ME, HARETH. AS I FREED YOU.
LET ME END HER.
REAP HELL UPON EACH OTHER AND GROVEL IN THE BITING WASTE.

SEBASTIAN A. JONES   PETER BERGTING

THE UNTAMED

A Sinner's Prayer

STORY STRANGER

OASIS BURNS AS IT DID UPON MY LAST DAY LIVING. WHEN BABES AND BUTCHERS WERE BLOODIED ALIKE.

WHERE NONE WERE SAFE FROM A FATHER'S WRATH, A HUSBAND'S PAIN.

ONCE MORE THE PEOPLE FLEE MY RECKONING.

I CARE NOT FOR THEM.

ONLY FOR MY FAMILY WHO WAITS BEYOND THE DARK.

AND THE CHILD WHO WAITS BELOW THE LAST STAGE UPON WHICH I DREW BREATH...

THE SNOW FALLS AS THE GODS ABOVE WAGE A WAR OF THEIR OWN. THE SEVENTH SOUL WILL BE SUNDERED THIS NIGHT AND YET...

I AM TRAPPED, SOMEWHERE BETWEEN HEAVEN AND HELL. AS IT WAS IN LIFE AND IN DEATH.

WHERE THE DEVIL DWELLS BELOW.

THEY WILL NOT
DIE WELL.

NO!
BELLO CHUUM SHEMLOK J'ARUKAS, UVANTIENNE
NNH!
THE DEVIL WILL HAVE HIS DUE.
YOU NEED ME TO KILL HER...
I BROUGHT YOU BACK TO KILL HER.

HOME, A WORLD AWAY I HAVE BURNED AND SHAMED. A SANCTUARY I YEARN FOR.

A DISTANT FAMILY I HAVE ALL BUT SLAIN.

YOU OKAY, BOY?

NEED A REST, OLD MAN.

IS THERE SALVATION, NOT FOR A RESTLESS SINNER, BUT FOR THEM...

FINALLY LEFT OASIS. FEELS GOOD. DON'T THINK I'LL MISS IT WHERE I'M HEADING. YOU EV - EVER MISS IT?

YOU DID A BRAVE THING BACK THERE.

I DO.

YOUR FA - FAMILY IS ALIVE, HARETH.

THINK IT'S ENOUGH?

HOW...

THE ANGEL WHO MAY
ONE DAY SAVE US ALL.

"YOU ARE GOING BACK FOR *HIS* CHILD, LADY ESSESSA."

I AM.

HOW LONG WERE YOU GIVEN?

UNTIL *HIS* WILL IS DONE.

A Stranger Returns
Hyoung Taek Nam